The Do[] Cockere[]

Published by The Cockerel Press

British Library Cataloguing in Publication Data
Dorking Museum & Heritage Centre
The Dorking Cockerel
ISBN 978-1-909871-02-1

All proceeds from the sale of this publication will go to Dorking Museum & Heritage Centre, 62 West Street, Dorking, Surrey RH4 1BS
www.dorkingmuseum.org.uk

With acknowledgement to research undertaken by Mary Day and published by the Dorking Local History Group, 1985, with thanks to Mrs. Belyavin, Patricia Bennett, Katie Dobson and David Sutton. Additional research and booklet written and prepared by David Burton.

Frontispiece: Dorking Cockerel by Peter Barnard, 1987, showing St Martin's Church and Leith Hill Tower.
From the collection of Dorking Museum & Heritage Centre.

THE
COCKEREL
PRESS

Dorking is truly proud of the famous 'Dorking Cock', a special and rare breed of male chicken recognised across the world. Dorking Museum has its own Dorkings, two magnificent birds preserved and displayed in a glass case close to the Museum entrance. Often known locally as 'the five-claw'd-un', a reference to the breed's particular distinguishing feature, the cock has become recognised as the town's symbol. Depictions can be seen throughout the town, most strikingly, a 10ft high silver cockerel that has graced the Deepdene roundabout since 2007.

Early origins

There has been much speculation about the origins of the Dorking breed. It is believed that it may have come from Italy during the period of the Roman Empire. This is largely based on the evidence of the 1st century AD Roman soldier, farmer and agricultural writer, Columella. He wrote of a square-formed hen, large and broad-breasted "and not with an even number of claws: they are reckoned the most generous which have five toes"[1]. Other early references were made by Pliny in Rome and Aristotle in Greece, and a third century AD Roman mosaic, found in Carnuntum (now in Austria), appears to show a five-toed rooster similar to the Dorking[2]. Centuries later, the Italian naturalist Ulisse Aldrovandi also wrote of the presence of the five-toed breed in Italy around 1600 AD.

Although there are some differences between the hens described by Columella and the Dorkings as identified later, most writers see a strong connection, whether or not these birds were already present in Britain or imported by the Romans. The noted 19th century writer, Lewis Wright, concluded that "the Dorking – as we know it now – is the more or less direct descendant of those birds which in old Columella's days were most prized by the poultry-keepers of Rome"[3].

John Martin's Rose Combed Dorking Cock, "Champion", a multiple cup-winner in 1870-72 at Stroud, Newport, Cheltenham, Southampton, Crystal Palace and Dublin. Martin was a highly successful exhibitor of Dorkings, initially as poultry-breeder to Viscountess Holmesdale, and later on his own account.

Illustration by J. W. Ludlow, from *The Illustrated Book of Poultry*, Lewis Wright, Cassell, Petter & Galpin, 1873

Growing reputation

For centuries, Surrey and Sussex were renowned for the quality of their poultry, raised on smallholdings, farms and estates and serving a growing demand from London. The capons served at medieval banquets shared many of the traits of the Dorking breed, and "the Dorking acquired a reputation for an especially tender meatiness, so that consumers requested them by name"[4].

Dorking itself became a centre for the poultry trade. In the 17th century, the antiquary and writer John Aubrey wrote of the Dorking market that "it is the greatest Market for Poultry in England"[5]. In the following century, commenting on the quantity of poultry sold in Dorking, one writer added that "they are well known to the lovers of good eating for being remarkably large and fine"[6].

Early in the 18th century, the novelist Daniel Defoe – who is believed to have attended a boarding school in Pixham Lane – made special mention of 'Darking' market and its famous poultry, "the name of a Darking Capon being well known among the poulterers in Leaden-Hall Market"[7].

This reputation continued well into the 19th century. In 1822, John Timbs noted that "an incredible quality of poultry is usually sold at the weekly markets. This trade is chiefly in the hands of a few individuals, who regularly attend, and supply the London dealers"[8].

Reminiscing early in the 20th century, Dorking miller and merchant John Attlee recalled the Thursday fowl markets in the first half of the 19th century, when "a great many farmers brought in fat fowls in crates; these fetched high prices and were eagerly bought up by higglers (dealers who bought and packed fattened poultry) for the London trade. The fowls were all of the old-fashioned large dark Dorking breed, which when crammed sold well"[9].

O.F. Cresswell's Silver-Grey Dorking Hen, prize-winner at Ashford and Birmingham, 1872.
Illustration by J. W. Ludlow, from *The Illustrated Book of Poultry*, Lewis Wright, Cassell, Petter & Galpin, 1873

Writing in the 1870s, but looking back to a period early in the century, South Street linen-draper Charles Rose recalled that "the poultry extended from opposite the present Post Office (then at the corner of North Street) to the south of the Bull's Head Inn". He also reported that, at the time of writing, the Dorking Christmas Poultry show was still flourishing "as it certainly ought, in the town that has given a name to one of the most renowned breeds of poultry in the world"[10].

Dorking Cock Trivia: The Dorkings' fame in the mid-19th century was such that Edward Lear included references to "milk-white hens of Dorking" in his nonsense song *The Courtship of the Yonghy-Bonghy-Bò* in 1877. (His limericks also included *There was a Young Lady of Dorking*.)
Illustration: L. Leslie Brooke, from *The Jumblies and Other Nonsense Verses*, by Edward Lear, F Warne & Co., 1900, Project Gutenberg edition.

Dorking Cock Trivia: In 2009, US First Lady Michelle Obama started the first fruit and vegetable garden and apiary on the South Lawn of the White House. Yellow House Farm in New Hampshire offered the Obamas a small flock of White Dorkings. Unfortunately, it is illegal to keep chickens in Washington DC.
Picture: White Dorkings, Yellow House Farm, www.yellowhousefarmnh.com, with thanks to Joseph Marquette

John Martin's Single-combed Dorking Hen, first prize winner at Warrington, 1871.
Illustration by J. W. Ludlow, from *The Illustrated Book of Poultry*, Lewis Wright, Cassell, Petter & Galpin, 1873

The Victorian age

The Victorian era heralded a passion for studying, breeding and exhibiting poultry. By this time, "before the poultry-fancy had been heard or thought of, the Dorking had been bred to a high standard of perfection, simply as a fowl for the table" and become "the favourite table breed of those best of all judges, the London poulterers"[11].

Queen Victoria is said to have particularly favoured the Dorking, not just for its plentiful, tender white meat, but also for its delicately textured white eggs. In 1900, it was reported that something was amiss with the Queen when even the Dorking eggs served for her breakfast could make her feel uncomfortable. (It is one of very few breeds with red ear-lobes that produces a white-shelled egg.)

The surge in interest in poultry breeding led to the first poultry show organised by the Zoological Society in London in 1845. With their impressive appearance, the *Grey* or *Speckled* Dorkings won their class at this show and continued to win further national and local shows as interest grew. Famous prints of the time by Harrison Weir and J. W. Ludlow show proud Dorkings in their prime.

With the interest in producing show birds, breeders continued to develop colours and structure. The world's first book of poultry Standards was produced by the Poultry Club in London in 1865[12], presenting official standards for use by judges at poultry shows to try to maintain uniformity. It included only a limited number of breeds, but recognised three varieties of Dorking – the *Silver Grey, Colored* (sic) and *White*. Later, the *Red* – considered by many as the earliest – and the *Cuckoo* Dorkings were also accepted as principal varieties.

Miss Fairhurst's White Dorkings, prize-winners at Colchester, 1873.
Illustration by J. W. Ludlow, from *The Illustrated Book of Poultry*, Lewis Wright, Cassell, Petter & Galpin, 1873

All are characterised by distinctive colourings. There has long been dissension as to which came first, and breeders and enthusiasts fiercely debated their relative claims and merits in the Victorian press.

The *Silver Grey* cock has a silvery-white neck, back and wings with its black tail and breast having a blue-green sheen, while the hen is silver-grey with a salmon breast. The *Coloured* (or *Dark*) Dorking is a darker version of the Silver Grey, the hen having a salmon breast with black markings, brown wing feathers and a black back. The *White* Dorking has long been prized for the purity of its white plumage. The *Red* Dorking is a glossy dark red with a black tail and breast. The *Cuckoo* Dorking is light grey with blue-grey pencilling. A number of other colour variants have also been evidenced.

The Silver Grey and Red Dorkings have a 'single' comb (a straight row of spikes), the White and Cuckoo Dorkings a 'rose' comb (flatter and closer to the head). The Coloured or Dark Dorking can have either. In 1859, Charles Darwin cited the comb of the Dorking fowl as a key characteristic to be carefully maintained if the breed is not to degenerate[13]. (Darwin spent some time and wrote at Leith Hill Place – his sister was the wife of Josiah Wedgwood, and he was also the great-uncle of another Leith Hill Place resident, the composer Ralph Vaughan-Williams.)

The other most noted characteristic of the Dorking is, of course, its fifth toe. It does not seem to serve any useful purpose and is placed just above the fourth toe, pointing upwards. It is present in only four other poultry breeds as standard.

With the high regard in which the Dorking was held, it is perhaps not surprising that it was also used in the development of the Sussex, Orpington and various other breeds.

Detail of one of Dorking Museum's own preserved Dorking Cocks, on display close to the Museum entrance. Photo: Royston Williamson

Further afield

With the enthusiasm for the Dorking in Britain, it is not surprising that the breed found its way overseas and became popular in the US, Canada, Australia and elsewhere.

It is reported that Dorkings went with the early settlers to America, perhaps with the *Mayflower* (1620), and became popular on early American homesteads. It was one of the most common US farm birds in the 1800s. However, as in Britain, there was an upsurge of interest in poultry breeding in the 1840s and the Dorking was much sought after. They could be difficult to acquire from Britain, and it was reported that Dorking breeders would not send live birds, other than capons. One account suggests that, after trying for two years, it was only possible to arrange a shipment in 1847 with the assistance of a Dorking clergyman, Mr Courtney[14].

Dorkings were shown at the first poultry show in the US in 1849. One writer in 1852 refers to the "hen fever which has raged in New England very severely during the last two years" and that, "as a market or table fowl, the Dorkings stand very high, perhaps No. 1"[15].

In 1874, the American Poultry Association admitted the Silver Gray, Colored and White varieties into the *American Standard of Perfection.* The Red and Cuckoo varieties were not added until the 1990s.

Dorking Cock Trivia: A Dorking Cock geranium, raised by Sidney White of Dorking, made its debut at the 1971 Chelsea Show, and, according to *Garden News,* was "instantly acclaimed by geranium experts" as "the most talked-about tri-colour geranium in years". It attracted further headlines when a cutting was stolen from the show.

Prize 'Dark' Dorkings, and Red Dorkings, the property of Mr. Harry Hamlin, Edenbridge, Kent. Illustrations by Harrison Weir, from *Our Poultry*, Hutchinson & Co., 1902

'Big Jim'. Photo by Kim Consol, Star*Rose Ranch, California, www.starroseranch.com, from the website of Dorking Breeders Club, USA, http://dorkingbreedersclub.webs.com

Ensuring survival

Since its heyday in the 19th century, the commercial market for the pure Dorking breed has declined, with numbers falling throughout the 20th century. This is variously attributed to extensive cross-breeding, changing fashions in preferences for the table and for show, and the advent of faster growing crossbred strains of laying and meat birds.

It is now included on the Rare Breeds Survival Trust's list of UK poultry breeds 'at risk'. It is categorised as 'threatened' on the American Livestock Breeds Conservancy Conservation Priority List and 'critical' by Rare Breeds Canada. The Rare Breeds Trust of Australia included the Silver Grey in its list of the top ten poultry rare breeds. The Rare Breeds Survival Trust and Farm Animal Genetic Resources Committee estimate that there are fewer than 1,000 breeding females remaining in the UK, with the White and Cuckoo variants particularly at risk from declining numbers and inbreeding problems[16].

However, it continues to engage the interest and loyalty of specialist breeders and heritage centres around the world. The Dorking Breed Club in the UK monitors bird numbers amongst its members, several of whom are in the local area[17]. Overseas, there are also Dorking clubs not just in the US, Canada and Australia, but in France, Germany, Denmark and the Netherlands. At working farms, thriving flocks of Dorkings may be found, for example, at the Acton Scott Working Farm Museum in Shropshire, and, in the US, at Colonial Williamsburg, the Plimoth Plantation's Rare Breeds programme and the Oliver H. Kelley Farm in Minnesota.

Dorking Cock Trivia: In 2009, in the USA, the first ever heritage Chicken Choosin', sponsored by the American Livestock Breeds Conservancy and other organisations, was designed to highlight the culinary value of rare chicken breeds. The people's choice was hands down the Dorking.

The Dorking Cockerel at Deepdene Roundabout: Dorking's 'guerrilla knitters' deck it out to celebrate seasons or events. Main photo: Mark Percy, licensed to use under a Creative Commons Licence. Others celebrating the Jubilee, June 2012 (Sam Blackledge), Olympic Games, July 2012, Easter, March 2013 (Ian Stronge), Christmas, December 2012 (Grant Melton). Images reproduced by permission of The Dorking Advertiser.

As an emblem

The success of the Dorking breed quickly led to the *Silver Grey* standing as an emblem for the town itself. It featured in an advertisement for Dorking Sauce, prepared by E & F Durant, chemists of Dorking, as early as 1855[18]. It appeared on the town seal in 1894 and heraldic recognition came when it appeared on Dorking Urban District Council's coat of arms in 1951, and, on its formation, that of Mole Valley District Council in 1975.

The bird has long been used as an emblem for local businesses, clubs and associations, covering commerce,

THE CELEBRATED

DORKING SAUCE,

For Game, Chops, Hashes, Hot and Cold Meat, Fish, Soups, Gravies, Curries, &c.

This delicious Condiment, which possesses a peculiar and agreeable piquancy, is, from the superiority of its zest, more generally useful than any other yet introduced, and is besides, from its valuable stomachic qualities, greatly calculated to facilitate digestion.

Prepared only by

E. & F. DURANT, LATE HARRISON,
Chemists, Dorking,

And may be obtained of all respectable Chemists and Grocers throughout the Kingdom.

PRICE ONE SHILLING.

Dorking Sauce advertisement c 1855
From *A Hand-book of Dorking,* John Dennis, 1855, first published by John Rowe, republished by Kohler & Coombes, 1974

sports, the arts and leisure (see overleaf). It has been closely associated with Dorking Football Club, formed in 1880 and known as 'The Chicks'. A number of depictions of the Dorking Cock will be found on artefacts, drawings and photographs held by Dorking Museum, including output from the Dorking Foundry, whose former premises the Museum now occupies.

Around Dorking, you will catch sight of the Cock. It graces the weather-cock on the spire of St Martin's Church, road signs as you enter the town, signs for the Dorking Heritage Trails, and, of course, the 10ft high Dorking Cock which stands on the Deepdene roundabout. Though considered controversial by some, it earned blacksmith Peter Parkinson the Worshipful Company of Blacksmiths' Tonypandy Cup for the most outstanding piece of public work in metal for 2007/08.

A collection of emblems and badges of local organisations, in the collection of Dorking Museum. Photos: Royston Williamson.

References

[1] *Of Husbandry,* an English translation of Columella's two main works, *De Re Rustica* and *De Arboribus,* Millar, 1745.

[2] Shown in *A History of Domesticated Animals,* F. E. Zeuner, Harper & Row, 1963.

[3] Lewis Wright, *The Illustrated Book of Poultry,* Cassell, Petter & Galpin, 1873.

[4] Janet Vorwald Dohner, *The Encyclopedia of Historic and Endangered Livestock and Poultry Breeds*, Yale University Press, 2001.

[5] John Aubrey, *The Natural History and Antiquities of the County of Surrey, Begun in the year 1673,* E. Curll, 1718.

[6] 'A writer in 1763' from the Gentleman's Magazine, quoted in *The Poultry Book,* Rev. W. Wingfield and G. W. Johnson, W. S. Orr, 1853.

[7] Daniel Defoe, *A tour thro' the whole island of Great Britain,* 1724-26, republished JM Dent & Co., 1927.

[8] John Timbs, A *Picturesque Promenade Round Dorking, in Surrey,* John Warren, 1822.

[9] John Attlee, *Reminiscences of Old Dorking*, published in the Dorking Advertiser, 1912, republished by A.W. and W. Eade, 1952, collected in *Memories of Old Dorking*, Kohler & Coombes, 1977.

[10] Charles Rose, *Recollections of Old Dorking,* published 1876-78, collected in *Memories of Old Dorking*, Kohler & Coombes, 1977.

[11] Lewis Wright, *The Illustrated Book of Poultry,* Cassell, Petter & Galpin, 1873.

[12] *The Standard of Excellence in Exhibition Poultry, Authorized by the Poultry Club,* Editor: William Bernhard Tegetmeier, Groombridge and Sons, 1865

[13] Charles Darwin, *On The Origin of Species,* John Murray, 1859.

[14] *The American Agriculturalist, Volume IV,* Editor: A. B. Allen, Saxton & Miles, 1847.

[15] T. B. Miner, *The Journal of Agriculture,* January 7, 1852.

[16] Rare Breeds Survival Trust, www.rbst.org.uk, with thanks to Claire Barber, Conservation Officer.

[17] The Dorking Breed Club, www.vicvet.com/dorkingclub, with thanks to Victoria Roberts, Hon Sec.

[18] John Dennis, *A Hand-book of Dorking,* John Rowe, 1855, reprinted by Kohler & Coombes, 1974.

THE DORKING COCKEREL

The Dorking Cockerel by Roz Moseling (2012)